RHENEAS

Based on *The Railway Series* by the Rev. W. Awdry

Illustrations by
Robin Davies and Jerry Smith

EGMONT

EGMONT

We bring stories to life

First published in Great Britain in 2006
by Egmont UK Limited
239 Kensington High Street, London W8 6SA
This edition published in 2008
All Rights Reserved

HiT entertainment

ISBN 978 1 4052 3482 5
1 3 5 7 9 10 8 6 4 2
Printed in Italy

This is the story of Rheneas, a little engine who works high up in the mountains. Rheneas used to moan that he never had any important work to do, until he realised that all jobs on the railway are important ...

One morning, Rusty stopped to talk to Rheneas, who was sitting in a siding all on his own.

"Hello, Rheneas," said Rusty. "No passengers?"

Rheneas frowned. "I used to pull important trains," he said sadly. "Now I don't take passengers often. The Fat Controller said I deserved a rest, but that was a long time ago."

Just then, Rusty's Driver came along. "Time to go mend some tracks, Rusty," he said.

"Goodbye, Rheneas. I hope you'll cheer up soon," said Rusty.

Later that same morning, The Fat Controller came to the sheds. "I have a very important job for you today, Rheneas," he said.

Rheneas was very surprised. "An important job!" he cried. "Oh, thank you, Sir."

"I want you to take the children on a school trip into the mountains," The Fat Controller explained. "I'll see you at the Refreshment Lady's tea rooms afterwards."

"Yes, Sir," said Rheneas. But he was disappointed.

When Rheneas arrived at the station, the children and their teacher were waiting on the platform.

"A school trip into the mountains," he moaned to Rusty. "That's not an important job at all."

"Yes it is," said Rusty. "All the jobs on the railway are important."

Rheneas didn't agree. He had seen all the sights many times before. He was worried that there was nothing exciting or important to show the children.

The Fat Controller had told Rheneas' Driver to stop at all the sights around the Island of Sodor.

The first stop was the old bridge. "This bridge was built a very long time ago," his Driver announced. "It carries engines and trucks across the valley and into the mountains."

"Ooh," said the children.

But Rheneas had seen the bridge lots of times before, he didn't think it was exciting.

"Next stop is the viaduct," said the Driver.

Driver put on the brakes and Rheneas stopped on the viaduct.

"Look at the wonderful view!" said the children together.

"You can see all over Sodor," Driver explained.

Rheneas was still unhappy. To him, the trip didn't seem wonderful at all. "I must think of something important to show them," he puffed to himself.

Meanwhile, Rusty was busy repairing a small branch line.

The Foreman inspected the rails. He saw that the heavy rains had shifted the ground from under the tracks.

"This line must be closed until it is repaired," he said. "It is too dangerous for regular runs."

He put up a sign to warn other engines not to use the line.

"Let's get to work straight away," said Rusty.

Rheneas was in a hurry as he reached the points. He had made so many stops. First, the old bridge, then the viaduct and then the lake. He was afraid he would be late for The Fat Controller.

"I'll make up time, I'll make up time," he puffed.

But the Signalmen had forgotten to switch the points. Suddenly, Rheneas found himself on the dangerous track.

"Oh, no!" cried Rheneas' Driver.

Rheneas rocketed straight past Rusty. He couldn't stop – Rheneas was out of control!

"Keep your steam up!" cried Rusty, looking worried.

"Hooray!" cheered the children, as they bumped over the tracks.

Rheneas puffed bravely up the hill. The ground was shaking beneath his wheels.

"C-courage … c-courage … c-courage," he chuffed. Then he rattled down the other side.

He was determined to deliver his passengers safely.

The children squealed in delight, as Rheneas steamed over a rickety bridge.

But their teacher was worried. She didn't like heights and shut her eyes.

Rheneas was going faster and faster along the wobbly track. Driver gave a warning blast on the whistle. "PEEP! PEEP!"

It was the most exciting school trip the children had ever been on. "This is fun!" they cheered.

When Rheneas reached the waterfall, water splashed on to his passengers. They didn't mind at all and laughed happily. All except the teacher.

Rheneas rocked around a tight bend and could see the station up ahead. "Not far to go … not far to go," he chuffed.

It was such a bumpy journey that the teacher's hat flew off and blew into a field, where a goat ate it for tea!

At last, Rheneas pulled into the platform. The Fat Controller was waiting to greet him.

"That was the best school trip ever!" the children told The Fat Controller. Their teacher wasn't so sure.

"Well done, Rheneas," said The Fat Controller. "You brought your passengers back safely – that is what is important."

Rheneas beamed with pride. Now he knows that all the jobs on the railway are important.

The Thomas Story Library is THE definitive collection of stories about Thomas and ALL his friends.

5 more Thomas Story Library titles will be chuffing into your local bookshop in August 2008!

Jeremy
Hector
BoCo
Billy
Whiff

And there are even more Thomas Story Library books to follow later

So go on, start your Thomas Story Library NOW!

A Fantastic Offer for Thomas the Tank Engine Fans!

STICK
POUND
COIN
HERE

In every Thomas Story Library book like this one,
you will find a special token. Collect 6 Thomas
tokens and we will send you a brilliant Thomas
poster, and a double-sided bedroom door hanger!
Simply tape a £1 coin in the space above, and fill out
the form overleaf.

TO BE COMPLETED BY AN ADULT

To apply for this great offer, ask an adult to complete the coupon below
and send it with a pound coin and 6 tokens, to:
THOMAS OFFERS, PO BOX 715, HORSHAM RH12 5WG

☐ Please send a Thomas poster and door hanger. I enclose 6 tokens
plus a £1 coin. (Price includes P&P)

Fan's name..

Address..

....Postcode...........................

Date of birth...

Name of parent/guardian..

Signature of parent/guardian...

Please allow 28 days for delivery. Offer is only available while stocks last. We reserve the right to change
the terms of this offer at any time and we offer a 14 day money back guarantee. This does not affect your
statutory rights.

☐ Data Protection Act: If you do not wish to receive other similar offers from us or companies we
recommend, please tick this box. Offers apply to UK only.

Cut along the dotted line